FAVOURITE TALES FROM THE
QURAN

TWO TALES:
In the Beginning
First Man and Woman

Saniyasnain Khan

GOODWORD

In the Beginning

Long long ago, there was no earth, no
sky, no sun or moon. There was
darkness everywhere. Then Allah
thought of making a beautiful world—a
world full of purpose.

Allah just said the words and there was the earth and the sky. There was the bright sun, the shining moon and twinkling stars. Then came the dry land and the oceans. By just saying the words, Allah made them all. Allah made the earth in two days. On it He placed very big mountains.

In two days He formed the sky into seven heavens. The lowest heaven He hung with brilliant stars and sent bright comets flying between them. Allah made the earth circle around the sun so that there would be night and day and many different seasons too. Allah filled the vast universe with thousands of stars and many planets all spinning swiftly, but never touching each other.

Allah made lovely flowers—roses and pansies, bluebells and lupins, hollyhocks and daisies. Where did the flowers come from? Allah made them all. He made all things large and tiny. Little insects, and black ants that crawl around on the ground. And the busy bees that fly from flower to flower to collect sweet honey.

Allah made juicy fruits—mangoes, oranges and cherries, crunchy apples, sweet grapes and soft bananas. Where did the fruits come from? Allah made them all.

Allah made the animals. Some live in the forests. Large elephants, fat hippos, cunning foxes, fierce tigers, striped zebras and tall giraffes. Fluffy rabbits, strong horses, grazing cows and sheep— Allah made them all.

Beautiful birds flying in the sky—
spreading their wings and closing them.
Green parrots, white ducks, colourful
chickens, flying sparrows, dancing
peacocks, singing quails, diving
kingfishers, warbling larks, and many,
many more. Where did they all come
from? Allah made them all.

Allah made the large oceans and the big
seas which cover the earth with water
and form into deep lakes and long
rivers. Allah made the sea monsters and
all the fishes big and small—large blue
whales like mountains, and cruel tiger
sharks with big jaws.

Allah made the crabs and lobsters and shrimps, huge eels and octopuses, swordfish and jellyfish, and all the many ocean plants and animals.

15

Allah gave us rain and sunshine, cool breezes and clouds passing by.

Thank You, Allah, for making such a
wonderful world.

17

The First Man and Woman

Long long ago, Allah created the beautiful universe, full of galaxies, planets, the moon, and stars all moving in harmony, all glorifying and praising Him.

When Allah decided to create a human being, He collected every kind of soil and mixed it like a potter's clay.

19

Moulding it into the shape of a man,
Allah breathed His spirit into it.
In this way, He gave life to the first
man. The father of all of us. Allah
named him Adam عليه السلام.

Today, people may all be of different
colors, shapes and sizes, speaking
different languages and living in
different places. But they all have the
same ancestor—the first man, Adam عليه السلام.
Allah made him the first prophet
to guide people.

Allah bestowed many gifts upon Adam ﷺ. He gave him the gift of sight so that he might marvel at the creation of Allah, and the senses of hearing, smell, taste and touch to help him understand the universe around him. Apart from all these blessings, Allah gave him the intelligence to be able to tell what was right and what was wrong and made him

capable of doing good works. With this
Allah gave him knowledge and wisdom
and put him above the angels.

Allah also created the first woman,
Hawwa (Eve) as a helper and loving
companion of Adam ﷺ. He told the
couple to live in the garden of Paradise,
but warned them not to approach a
particular tree. Both of them
began living there
in perfect peace
and happiness,
with dazzling
beauty all around
them.

But Satan was jealous of them, seeing the honour they received from Allah. So one day, he came to Adam ﷺ and his wife and whispered to them, tempting them to approach the forbidden tree. He told them that it was the tree of eternal life, and that if they ate from it, they would never grow old, nor would they ever die.

Satan made them believe that he was giving them very friendly advice, so they ate from the tree and became wrongdoers. But no sooner had they done so, than they realized their fault and immediately turned towards Allah to say how sorry they were.

Allah forgave them both, but told them that since they had defied His orders, they would have to leave the gardens of Paradise and go down to earth. There Adam ﷺ and Hawwa found themselves all alone, for no one else was living on the earth at that time.

Allah told them that from time to time His messengers and prophets would be coming to the earth to guide people to the true path. Those who followed His directions and lived a good life would have no fear on the Judgement Day and would be admitted to Paradise. But those

who disbelieved and rejected Allah's signs would be taken to task and thrown into the fire of Hell.

The story of the Prophet Adam عليه السلام teaches us that we have all been created by Allah, and that therefore, we are all equal. We should, then, respect each and

every human being and never look down
on others, or insult people. After all, we
are all the children of one forefather—
the Prophet Adam ﷺ.

ﷺ *Alayhis Salam* 'May peace be upon him.'
The customary blessing on the prophets.